ALBERT O'BALSAM and his MAGIC HAT

ALBERT O'BALSAM WAS LOOKING IN HIS ATTIC FOR HIS HEIRLOOM BUS TICKET ONE FINE DAY...

HELLO ~ WHAT'S THIS?

A HAT? AND A NOTE WRITTEN IN CRAYON ON TOILET PAPER!

"DEAR ALBERT, I WANT YOU TO HAVE MY MAGIC HAT NOW THAT THE DOCTORS WON'T LET ME KEEP IT ANY MORE. USE IT'S POWERS WISELY ~ SIGNED, YOUR GREAT-UNCLE GOBFREY "NUTTER" O'BALSAM, WARD THIRTEEN, EAST WING."

CRIKEY! I WONDER WHAT WOULD HAPPEN IF I PUT IT ON?

THERE WE ARE!

UNCLE GOBFREY ~ I'M GOING TO FOLLOW IN YOUR FOOTSTEPS! I'M GOING TO GO FOR A WALK AND LET MAGICAL THINGS HAPPEN!

SOON...

HELLO LITTLE URCHIN! IS THAT A FROG YOU'RE CARRYING?

SHOVE OFF, BIGNOSE!

RIBBET

COME, COME NOW, YOUNG RAGAMUFFIN ~ ALL I ASK IS THAT YOU LET ME KISS YOUR FROG AND BREAK IT FREE OF ITS ENCHANTMENT!

IF YOU TOUCH ME I'LL SCREAM! MY MUM WARNED ME ABOUT PEOPLE LIKE YOU!

OH YEAH? WELL YOU'VE JUST BLOWN YOUR THREE WISHES, PUNK!

YAMPY AS THE DAY IS LONG

WAAAHHH

A BIT LATER...

AHA! ~ NOW WHAT IS THIS I SEE?

BOUNCE!

10.

OFFICIAL
RED DWARF
T.SHIRTS

1358 RED DWARF SMEG HEAD

CHILDRENS SIZES

£5.99

SMALL AND MEDIUM

AVAILABLE IN
ADULT SIZES ONLY

1585 KIPPER   1357 BETTER THAN LIFE

LARGE AND X.LARGE £8.99

FELIX
and his
AMAZING UNDERPANTS

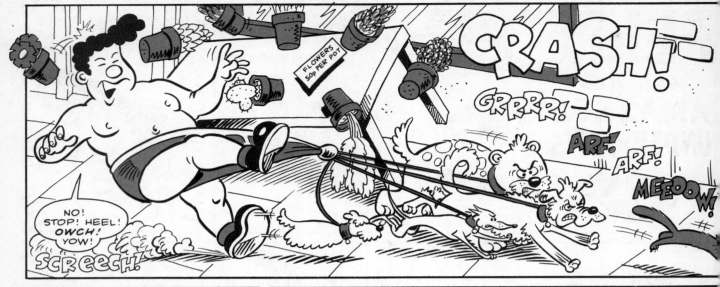

CRASH!

GRRRR!

ARF!

ARF!

MEEOOW!

NO! STOP! HEEL! OWCH! YOW!

SCREECH!

LATER... PAYING FOR THOSE BROKEN FLOWER POTS HAS LEFT ME *PENNYLESS!* OH WELL, I'LL GIVE IT ONE MORE GO.

AND SO...

OH DEAR. MY POOR OLD LEGS ARE TO *WEAK* AND *FEEBLE* TO CARRY THESE BAGS ALL THE WAY HOME FROM THE SUPERMARKET.

I'LL HELP YOU, USING MY *AMAZING UNDERPANTS!*

WHY, FELIX! THESE UNDERPANTS OF YOURS ARE SIMPLY... *AMAZING.!!*

I KNOW. CAREFUL YOU DON'T *CRACK YOUR EGGS!*

FELIX, MY NAME IS DORIS POMTIN, MOTHER OF BILLY POMTIN — THE FAMOUS HOLIDAY CAMP OWNER. BECAUSE YOU'VE BEEN SO KIND TO ME I'M GOING TO ASK BILLY TO GIVE YOU *A FREE HOLIDAY* AT POMTIN'S HOLIDAY CAMP!

CRICKEY! JUST WHAT I *WANTED!*

AND SO, THE NEXT DAY, FELIX IS ON THE COACH BOUND FOR POMTIN'S HOLIDAY CAMP...

BRUMMMM!

POMTINS

THE COAST!

...AND HE ENTERTAINS HIS FELLOW PASSENGERS BY PLAYING A TUNE ON HIS AMAZING UNDERPANTS...

TWANG TWANG

...TEN GREEN BOTTLES HANGING ON THE WALL... TEN GREEN BOTTLES HANGING ON THE WALL...

14.

FINALLY THE COACH ARRIVES AT POMTIN'S HOLIDAY CAMP...

I'LL CARRY THE LUGGAGE FOR THE CAMPERS. IT'S EASY WHEN YOU HAVE AN AMAZING PAIR OF UNDER-PANTS! THEIR LUGGAGE HANDLING CAPACITY IS *ENORMOUS.*

I'D BETTER FIND BARRY POMTIN AND THANK HIM FOR GIVING ME THIS FREE HOLIDAY.

FELIX FINDS BARRY POMTIN ON HIS OWN PRIVATE GOLF COURSE.

THANK YOU FOR GIVING ME THIS *FREE HOLIDAY,* MR. POMTIN.

THWACK!

THAT'S ALL RIGHT, FELIX, YOU DESERVE IT FOR HELPING MY DEAR, FEEBLE, OLD MOTHER.

BUT WHEN *BARRY POMTIN* PICKS UP HIS EXPENSIVE GOLF CLUBS...

OH NO! MY GOLF BAG HAS SUDDENLY, AND FOR NO APPARENT REASON, BROKEN! HOW AM I GOING TO CARRY MY EXPENSIVE GOLF CLUBS NOW?

DON'T WORRY, MR. POMTIN. I THINK I CAN HELP.

RIP!

CRASH!

AND SO...

HAVING A PAIR OF AMAZING UNDERPANTS CERTAINLY DOES COME IN HANDY, FELIX.

YES! AND THEY ALSO HELP TO KEEP MY BOTTOM WARM.

AFTER MR. POMTIN FINISHES HIS ROUND OF GOLF FELIX HEADS FOR THE BEACH...

BRILLIANT! I CAN'T WAIT TO RELAX ON THOSE CALM OCEAN WAVES.

AND SO...

THIS IS THE LIFE. NOTHING TO DO BUT RELAX AND SOAK UP THE SUN'S WARMING RAYS.

BUT THE SOOTHING OCEAN WAVES SOON ROCK FELIX TO SLEEP...

ZZZZZZZZZ

WARNING: DON'T EVER FALL ASLEEP WHEN YOU'RE FLOATING ON THE OCEAN!

15.

MUCH LATER... OH DEAR, I MUST HAVE DOZED OFF. I'D BETTER GET BACK TO THE HOLIDAY CAMP FOR MY TEA.

BUT TO HIS HORROR FELIX DISCOVERS THAT HE HAS DRIFTED MILES OUT TO SEA AND IS TOTALLY LOST!

OH NO! I'VE DRIFTED MILES OUT TO SEA AND I'M TOTALLY LOST!

WHAT INGENIOUS UNDERPANT UTILIZATION WILL GET ME OUT OF THIS SCRAPE?

FELIX CLEVERLY USES HIS AMAZING UNDERPANTS AS A SAIL, AND SOON...

LAND AHOY! THERE'S A SMALL ISLAND JUST AHEAD. I'LL LAND THERE AND WAIT TO BE RESCUED.

BUT!

OH CRICKEY! HOW SILLY OF ME IT'S NOT AN ISLAND AT ALL, IT' A WHALE, AND IT'S COMING THIS WA

OOER! IT'S MISTAKEN MY UNDERPANTS FOR PLANKTON AND IS SWALLOWING ME!

GULP!

SPLOOSH!

AND SO, FELIX FINDS HIMSELF INSIDE THE CAVERNOUS STOMACH OF THE FRIENDLY, BUT NEARLY EXTINCT, OCEAN MAMMAL...

GOSH! I BET MOST PEOPLE NEVER GET THE CHANCE TO SEE WHAT A WHALE LOOKS LIKE FROM THE INSIDE!

BUT THEN...

CRICKEY! THIS CROWN IS MADE OUT OF SOLID GOLD! SO IS THIS SCEPTRE AND NECKLACE THEY MUST BE PART OF A VALUABLE SUNKEN TREASUR WHICH THE WHALE UNWITTINGLY SWALLOWE AT SOME POINT!

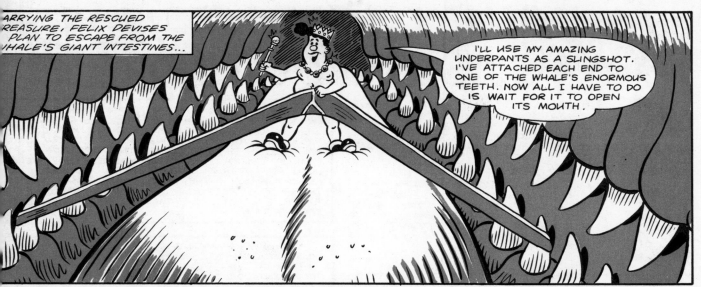

CARRYING THE RESCUED TREASURE, FELIX DEVISES A PLAN TO ESCAPE FROM THE WHALE'S GIANT INTESTINES...

I'LL USE MY AMAZING UNDERPANTS AS A SLINGSHOT. I'VE ATTACHED EACH END TO ONE OF THE WHALE'S ENORMOUS TEETH. NOW ALL I HAVE TO DO IS WAIT FOR IT TO OPEN ITS MOUTH.

AND SOON...

I HOPE I'M HEADING IN THE RIGHT DIRECTION FOR POMTIN'S HOLIDAY CAMP.

TWANG!

?

MEANWHILE, BACK AT THE HOLIDAY CAMP, BARRY POMTIN HAS NOTIFIED THE AUTHORITIES THAT FELIX IS MISSING...

OH DEAR. I DO HOPE NOTHING UNFORTUNATE HAS HAPPENED TO YOUNG FELIX.

THAT'S THE TROUBLE WITH THE YOUNGER GENERATION, MR. POMTIN, THEY THINK THEY KNOW IT ALL.

BUT THEN...

WOOORFF...MUFF... FLEEEK...GUFFFF...

SPLOSH

SPLOSH

GOOD GRIEF! IT'S A CREATURE FROM THE BOTTOM OF THE SEA!

THAT CROWN! THAT SEAWEED! IT'S NEPTUNE, GOD OF THE SEVEN SEAS!

NO, MR. POMTIN. IT'S ONLY ME, FELIX! WHILE I WAS SWIMMING ASHORE THIS OCTOPUS BECAME TRAPPED IN MY AMAZING UNDERPANTS AND I WAS COVERED IN SEAWEED.

AND SO...

I GOT A BIG REWARD FOR RECOVERING THE LOST TREASURE, AND MY PICTURE IN THE LOCAL PAPER. BUT FROM NOW ON I THINK I'LL STAY ON THE BEACH!

THE LOCAL ECHO

FELIX HAS A WHALE OF A TIME

FINDS SUNKEN TREASURE

FELIX'S AMAZING UNDERPANT FACT FILE!

HI, PANT FANS! FELIX HERE. AS YOU PROBABLY KNOW, I'M SOMETHING OF AN UNDERPANT EXPERT. SOME PEOPLE LISTEN TO RECORDS, SOME PEOPLE SPOT TRAINS, SOME PEOPLE COLLECT STAMPS. BUT I DON'T. I JUST WEAR UNDERPANTS.

HOW MUCH DO **YOU** KNOW ABOUT YOUR UNDERPANTS? BELIEVE IT OR NOT, UNDERPANTS ARE PRETTY INTERESTING THINGS. HERE'S A DOZEN **REALLY INTERESTING** THINGS I BET YOU NEVER KNEW ABOUT THEM...

1: THE FIRST PEOPLE TO WEAR UNDERPANTS WERE CAVEMEN. THEY LIVED IN COLD AND DRAUGHTY CAVES, AND WORE DINOSAUR-SKIN PANTS TO KEEP THEIR BOTTOMS AND PRIVATE PARTS WARM.

2: IN THE OLDEN DAYS, KNIGHTS IN SHINING ARMOUR WORE SPECIAL METAL UNDIES. IF THEY DIDN'T CHANGE THEM EVERY DAY, AND OIL THEM REGULARLY, THEY BECAME RUSTY AND THEIR BOTTOMS BECAME SORE.

3: UNDERPANTS AS WE KNOW THEM TODAY WERE INVENTED BY THE SIXTH EARL OF UNDERPANT IN 1783. HIS WIFE TOOK PITY ON THE SOLDIERS WHO HAD TO LOWER THEIR TROUSERS EVERY TIME THEY USED THE LAVATORY. TO SOLVE THE PROBLEM, THE EARL ISSUED ALL HIS SOLDIERS WITH SMART NYLON PANTS WITH A SPECIAL HOLE AT THE FRONT, ALLOWING THEM TO USE THE TOILET WITHOUT REMOVING THEIR PANTS.

4: DURING THE SECOND WORLD WAR, THERE WERE NO UNDERPANTS IN BRITAIN. THE GOVERNMENT COLLECTED THEM ALL, AND USED THEM FOR THE WAR EFFORT, TO MAKE PARACHUTES.

5: THE MOST EXPENSIVE UNDERPANTS IN THE WORLD ARE THE GRAND PANTS OF SIAM. THEY WERE A GIFT TO THE EMPEROR OF THAT COUNTRY FROM THE QUEEN, AND WERE KNITTED OUT OF SOLID GOLD THREAD, CONTAINING DOZENS OF PEARLS, EMERALDS, AND DIAMONDS. THEY WERE INSURED FOR AN INCREDIBLE £10 MILLION. UNFORTUNATELY, THE BIGGEST DIAMOND OF ALL, THE FAMOUS BOTTIKLEFT DIAMOND, FELL OFF AFTER THE EMPEROR FARTED, AND WAS NEVER SEEN AGAIN.

6: NOT ONLY IS FARTING RUDE, IT CAN ALSO BREAK YOUR UNDERPANTS! ESPECIALLY A BIG, LOUD ONE. (IF YOU DO FART, ALWAYS DO IT OUT OF EARSHOT OF PARENTS OR TEACHERS.)

7: DESPITE BEING THE RICHEST MAN IN BRITAIN, TERRY WOGAN ONLY HAS ONE PAIR OF UNDERPANTS WHICH HE WEARS ALL THE TIME. TERRY REMOVES THE PANTS ONCE A YEAR — ON CHRISTMAS DAY — AND WASHES THEM WITH INDUSTRIAL PANT CLEANER.

8: THE WORLD RECORD FOR THE MOST UNDERPANTS EVER WORN BY ONE PERSON IS FOUR PAIRS, HELD BY WALTER ROBSON OF TIVERTON IN DEVON. UNFORTUNATELY, AFTER PUTTING ON FOUR PAIRS OF PANTS, WALTER NEEDED THE LAVATORY, SO HE HAD TO TAKE THEM ALL OFF AGAIN.

9: NAPOLEON ALWAYS HAD ONE HAND INSIDE HIS JACKET. HISTORIANS NOW BELIEVE THIS WAS BECAUSE THE ELASTIC IN HIS UNDERPANTS HAD BEEN DAMAGED DURING A BATTLE, AND HE USED HIS HAND TO KEEP HIS PANTS UP.

10: ASTRONAUTS WHO FLY IN SPACE HAVE TO WEAR SPECIAL SPACE UNDERPANTS. UNLIKE NORMAL UNDERPANTS, SPACE UNDERPANTS HAVE NO ELASTIC — FOR IN SPACE THERE IS NO GRAVITY, AND UNDERPANTS HOLD THEMSELVES UP.

11: THE BEATLES MAY NOT HAVE BEEN SO SUCCESSFUL IF THEY HADN'T CHANGED THEIR NAME. FOR THE GROUP WERE ORIGINALLY KNOWN AS THE SWINGING UNDERPANTS. HOWEVER, PAUL McCARTNEY'S DAD TOLD HIM TO CHANGE THE NAME BECAUSE IN THE SIXTIES UNDERPANTS WERE CONSIDERED RUDE.

12: IF YOU PULL DOWN A FIREMAN'S TROUSERS, YOU WON'T FIND AN ORDINARY PAIR OF UNDERPANTS. THEY WEAR SPECIAL FIREPROOF PANTS MADE OUT OF TEFLON AND ASBESTOS. THEY ARE RED, WITH A YELLOW 'Y' ON THE FRONT, AND A SPECIAL BELL WHICH RINGS WHENEVER THE FIREMAN NEEDS THE TOILET.

SCRIPT: CHRIS DONALD • ART: LEW STRINGER

Captain Morgan and his HAMMOND ORGAN

SHIP AHOY, CAP'N!

AHARR! SHIVER ME TIMBERS! HOIST THE JOLLY ROGER ME HEARTIES!

'TIS A FAT SPANISH GALLEON, AN' HER BOWS BE BULGIN' WITH GOLD DOUBLOONS. HA-HAAAR! LET'S FILL OUR BELLIES WITH FINE SPANISH RUM, AND OUR POCKETS WITH GOLD.

AYE, CAP'N LET'S RAM HER AMIDSHIPS, AND CUT THEIR SCURVY THROATS!

AYE!

AYE!

HARD AS NAILS

ALL IN GOOD TIME - BUT FIRST LET'S HAVE A LITTLE TUNE ON ME HAMMOND ORGAN.

AWW, NO!

BO'SUN, HIT ME WITH A BOSSA NOVA RHYTHM...

A ONE, A TWO, A ONE-TWO-THREE-FOUR---

AYE...

...WONDER IF ONE DAY THAT... YOU'LL SAY THAT... YOU CARE...

...IF YOU SAY YOU'LL LOVE ME MADLY... I'D GLADLY... BE THERE LIKE A PUPPET ON A STRI-I-ING

...LIKE A PUPPET ON A DOO DOO DOO DOO DOO... DOOBY-DOOBY-DOO!

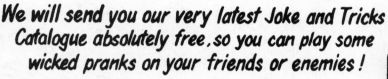

23.

ONE FINE DAY AT THE BEACH...

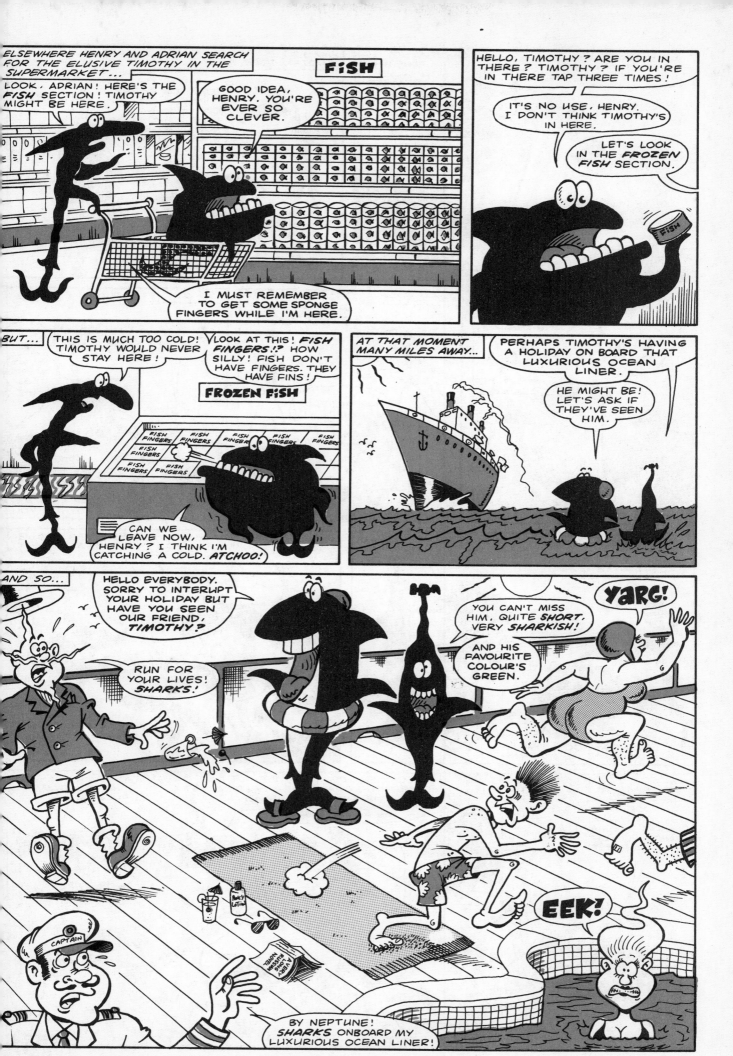

SOME HEDGEHOGS YOU JUST DON'T MESS WITH

SONIC THE HEDGEHOG

THE NEW HERO FOR THE SEGA 16 BIT MEGA DRIVE

DEAD TEACHER

Now I've got your attention here are some great gifts for little kids and big kids.

Frogs & Hippos £2.99. Pull the fish out of his mouth and watch him swim after it and gobble it up. Great bathtime fun.

Bart Simpson Mugs £3.99. Four different designs

Bart Phone £32.99. Barts eyes light up when in use.

Buzzle £9.99. Guide the wand around the electrified ring without touching the sides otherwise you get buzzed – battery operated.

Gumball Machine £39.99. Real American metal gumball machine takes any currency.

Fruit Machine £14.99. Takes money and pays out. More expensive one-armed bandits available – please phone for details.

My Little Fish £14.99. A mechanical fish that swims in its own bowl – as seen on TV – battery operated.

Pinhead £19.99. Thousands of pins create your own sculpture of your face and hands or anything you can think of.

Jumping Monkey £24.99. Clap your hands and the monkey will jump and squeak for 30 seconds – battery operated.

Newtons Cradle £6.99. Just like Mum and Dad used to have – five balls on string that move with each other.

Squirting Toilet £2.99. Get your sister to lift the lid and it squirts her with water.

Nurd £4.99. Don't hit your brother, hit the nurd. Squashy face that always comes back smiling.

Nurd Keyring £1.99. Squash and stretch this little fella – he loves it.

Fart Spray £1.99. It stinks!

Pool Table £9.99. Best quality, you can really play on it.

Basketball Hoop £4.99. Put it over your bin or desk and throw your homework in it.

World's Most Difficult Jigsaw Puzzle £9.99. Double sided torture.

Converse Trainer Telephone £39.99. This telephone is a real converse trainer.

Crazy Glasses £2.99. Put them on, dip one end in a drink then suck. The liquid goes around the seethru glasses – hilarious.

Off The Wall Clocks £12.99. When the alarm goes, throw it against the wall and it stops. Cricket, tennis, football or American football.

Fun Snaps 6 Packs £2.99. Throw them, snap them or stamp on them for a loud crack, 50 in a pack.

Inflatables – Banana £2.99, Shark & Crocodile £9.99, Hamburger £6.99, Guitar & Saxophone £5.99.

Jokes – blue mouth sweets, whoopee cushion, black face soap, snappy gum, itching, sneezing & farting powder, squirting ring, love potion, fart whistle, money snatcher and loads more. **8 for £5.00, 18 for £10.00.**

Add £2.00 p&p for all orders. 48 hour delivery.

We accept all major credit cards.

Phone today: 081-892 1600 or 0344 55575, Mon – Sat, 9.30 – 6.00, or send your cheque or postal order to 'Bananas', 18 Heath Road, Twickenham, Middlesex TW1 4BZ.

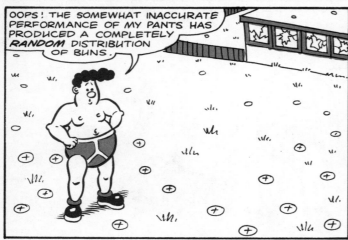

ALBERT O'BALSAM *and his* MAGIC HATS!

When we last saw Albert O'Balsam on page eleven, he was convinced that his hat possessed magic powers! However, in the absence of a single shred of evidence to support this theory, he's been forced to have a bit of a re-think...

NOW he believes that the hat counter in the local department store is magic, and if he tries on any hat, an adventure will immediately follow!

Good morning, sir — I wonder which hat I might try on today?

Mmm... let me see now...

A trilby, perhaps! Imagine the adventures that must hold in store!

...Or a beret — just think! I could suddenly find myself leading the brave resistance fighters in German-occupied France!

No... I think I'll go for this one — a deerstalker, as worn by the world's greatest detective, Sherlock Holmes!

No doubt the instant I pop it on my head I'll be whisked away into a magical land of mystery, murder, and intrigue in nineteenth century England!

That'll be £19.95, sir.

No... erm, sorry...

I... erm... have to try it on first... it's very important!

Well, go ahead then sir — put it on.

No... I have to try it on in the fitting room, you see!

Then, when I come out, my adventure begins!

Yes, if you say so sir... the fitting room is over there.

I'll try not to be too long, but you never can tell!

FITTING ROO

The PATHETIC SHARKS in: WINTER WARMER!

RUPERT

JUSTIN

ADRIAN

TIMOTHY

HENRY

BEHOLD THE DEPTHS OF THE SEA! A SAVAGE DOMAIN, POPULATED BY FIERCE AND MERCILESS CREATURES! A HIDDEN WORLD WHERE BLOODY CONFLICTS TAKE PLACE FAR BEYOND OUR CRUELIST IMAGINATIONS...

I TELL YOU IT'S NOT MY TURN TO DO THE WASHING UP! I'VE JUST DONE THE HOOVERING!

WELL DON'T LOOK AT ME! I'M WORN OUT AFTER DOING ALL THE DUSTING THIS MORNING!

IT'S TUESDAY! ADRIAN DOES THE WASHING UP ON TUESDAY!

I DID IT ON SUNDAY 'COS HENRY HAD A COLD!

Cave Sweet Cave

KNITTING WEEKLY

STORY + ART: LEW STRINGER.

41.

"OH NO! IT'S THE PATHETIC SHARKS!"
COOOEEH EVERYBODY! LOOK WHAT I'VE GOT! A NINETY NINE!
IT'S NOT FAIR! I WANT AN ICE CREAM WITH RASPBERRY SAUCE AND A SUGAR CONE!
I WANT AN ICE LOLLY! A "FAB 21" WITH HUNDREDS AND THOUSANDS ON IT!